THE WILL OF DARTH VADER

Designer
Tony Ong

Assistant Editor
Freddye Lins

Editor
Randy Stradley

Publisher
Mike Richardson

Special thanks to Jann Moorhead, David Anderman, Troy Alders, Leland Chee, Sue Rostoni, and
Carol Roeder at Lucas Licensing

STAR WARS ADVENTURES: THE WILL OF DARTH VADER

ISBN: 9781848566095

Published by Titan Books, a division of Titan Publishing Group Ltd.
144 Southwark Street, London SE1 0UP

Originally published by Dark Horse Comics.

A GIP catalogue record of this title is available from the British Library.

First edition: August 2010

10 9 8 7 6 5 4 3 2 1

Printed in Lithuania

THE WILL OF DARTH VADER

Script **Tom Taylor**

Pencils **Brian Koschak**

Inks **Dan Parsons**

Colours **Michael Wiggam**

Lettering **Michael Heisler**

Cover art **Sean McNally**

TITAN BOOKS

THIS STORY TAKES PLACE APPROXIMATELY THREE YEARS AFTER THE BATTLE OF YAVIN.

"ONE OF THE EMPIRE'S TRANSGALACTIC SUPPLY LINES IS NO LONGER SECURE. IMPERIAL CONVOYS ALONG THE CORELLIAN TRADE SPINE ARE SUFFERING ATTACKS AT THE HANDS OF A REBEL FORCE."

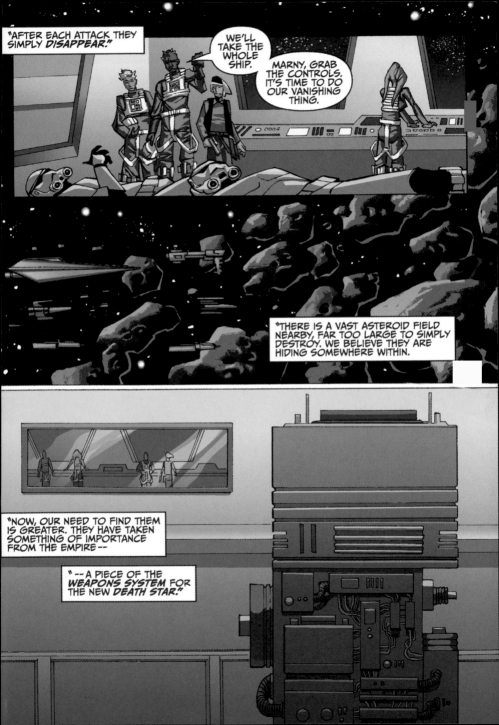

18

I HAVE NO INTEREST IN YOUR BANTER, *REBEL.*

REBEL? I'M NOT...*HCK*...A REBEL.

YOU WERE ENTERING *THEIR* TERRITORY.

I WAS BRINGING THEM... *CKK*...SUPPLIES. I DON'T...I DON'T CARE ABOUT....*KK*... YOUR WAR. I'M A... BUSINESSMAN.

IT WOULD BE...*CKK*...SO MUCH...EASIER... *UK*...TO TALK IF YOU WEREN'T...WEREN'T CRUSHING MY... THROAT!

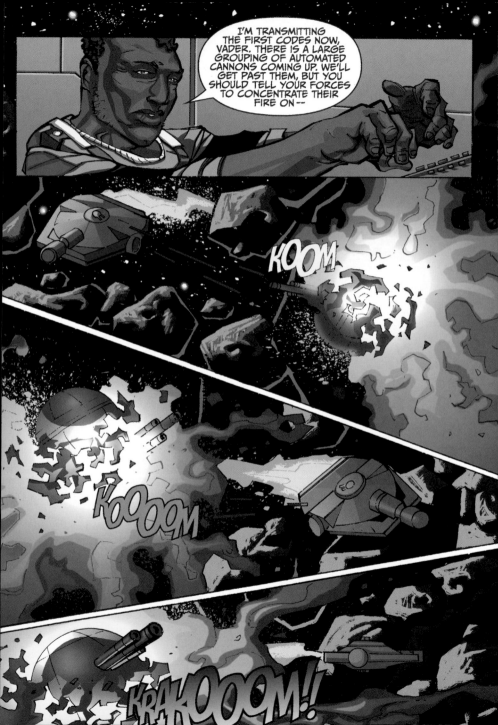

"WHEN I WAS A KID, I HAD A TOY SOLDIER.

"FOR A TIME, HE WENT EVERYWHERE WITH ME. IN MY HANDS, AND IN MY MIND, HE WAS UNSTOPPABLE.

"THAT TOY SOLDIER COMMANDED WHOLE FLEETS ACROSS CORELLIAN SKIES.

WWWWWWMWWWWMMMMMMM

WE SHOULDN'T BE OUT HERE UNPROTECTED. WE'LL NEED TO FIND A CAVE OR SOME OTHER SHELTER BEFORE NIGHTFALL. THERE'S A REASON THE REBEL BASE IS SO HEAVILY GUARDED -- AND IT HAS NOTHING TO DO WITH THE EMPIRE.

THERE ARE DANGEROUS OLD THINGS IN THIS PLACE.

DANGEROUS EVEN *COMPARED* TO YOU.

"SLEEP..."

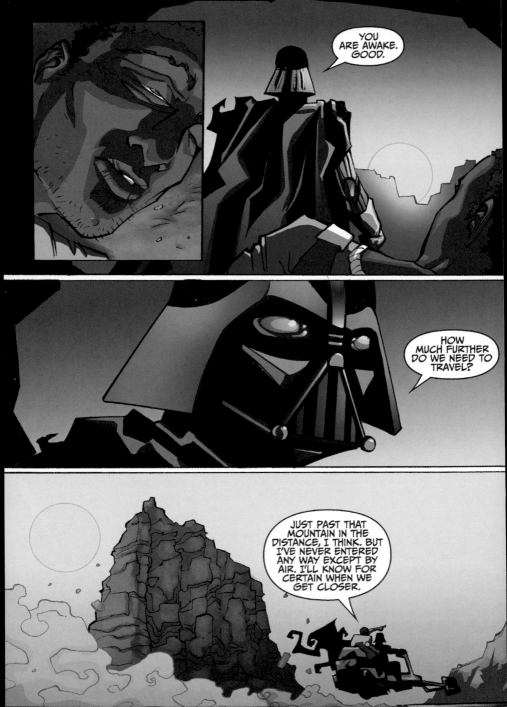

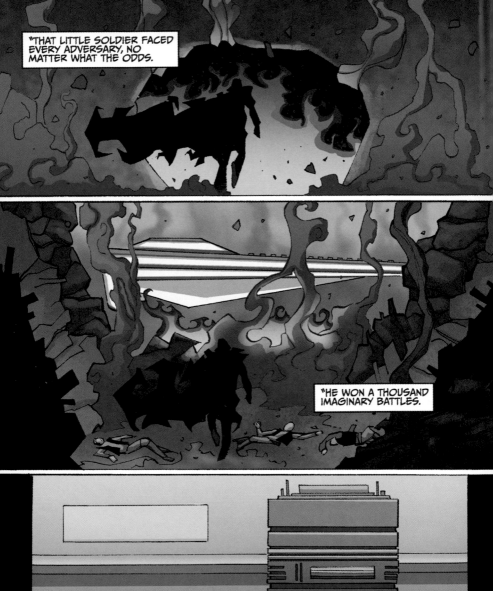

"THAT LITTLE SOLDIER FACED EVERY ADVERSARY, NO MATTER WHAT THE ODDS.

"HE WON A THOUSAND IMAGINARY BATTLES.

"THAT TOY SOLDIER COMMANDED WHOLE FLEETS ACROSS CORELLIAN SKIES.

"I CAST THAT TOY SOLDIER ASIDE AND NEVER THOUGHT OF HIM AGAIN --"

ALSO AVAILABLE NOW:

STAR WARS ADVENTURES

HAN SOLO AND THE HOLLOW MOON OF KHORYA
ISBN: 9781845769055

STAR WARS ADVENTURES

PRINCESS LEIA AND THE ROYAL RANSOM
ISBN: 9781845769550

STAR WARS ADVENTURES

LUKE SKYWALKER AND THE TREASURE OF THE DRAGONSNAKES
ISBN: 9781848564008

STAR WARS

THE CLONE WARS

SHIPYARDS OF DOOM

ISBN: 9781848561304

STAR WARS

THE CLONE WARS

CRASH COURSE

ISBN: 9781848562004

STAR WARS

THE CLONE WARS

THE WIND RAIDERS OF TALORAAN

ISBN: 9781848563346

STAR WARS

THE CLONE WARS

THE COLOSSUS OF DESTINY

ISBN: 9781848565371